THE THREE GOOD-LUCK CHARMS

Story retold by Hema Pande
Illustrations: Ram Waeerkar

THERE ARE MUCH BETTER CHESTNUTS GROWING IN MY GARDEN.

I'LL ROAST THE BIG, JUICY ONES AND BOIL THE TINY ONES FOR YOU.
THAT SOUNDS NICE.

THE OLD WOMAN TOOK THE BOY-MONK TO HER HOUSE AND GAVE HIM THE PROMISED TREAT.
THEY'RE DELICIOUS! BUT I CAN'T EAT ANY MORE...

YOU MUST BE SLEEPY. SLEEP HERE TONIGHT. YOU CAN GO BACK TO THE MONASTERY TOMORROW.

THE BOY-MONK GOT UNDER THE QUILT AND WAS SOON FAST ASLEEP.

AT MIDNIGHT, HE SUDDENLY AWOKE.
IT'S RAINING.

HE RAN BACK TO BED.
THE RAINDROPS SEEM TO BE SAYING SOMETHING.

PITTER PATTER LOOK AND SEE, THE OLD WOMAN SEEMS A WITCH TO ME...

THE BOY-MONK PEEPED OUT FROM UNDER THE QUILT.
THE OLD WOMAN... THERE SHE IS! WHAT IS SHE DOING?

HOW BEAUTIFUL I AM! HOW LONG AND SHARP MY HORNS HAVE GROWN!

IT'S THE MOUNTAIN WITCH!

SHE'LL EAT ME UP! I MUST ESCAPE IN THE MORNING.
THE BOY-MONK LAY AS STILL AS A STONE.

IN THE MORNING—
OLD WOMAN, I WANT TO HAVE A WASH.

IT'S TOO COLD FOR A WASH. STAY WHERE YOU ARE!

BUT OLD WOMAN, I MUST HAVE A WASH; I MUST; I SIMPLY MUST...

OH BOTHER! HOW MUCH YOU TROUBLE ME!

ALL RIGHT, GO! BUT I'LL TIE THIS ROPE ROUND YOUR WAIST.

NOW I MUST BE QUICK...

THEN HE TOOK OUT A GOOD-LUCK CHARM.

WHEN THE MOUNTAIN WITCH CALLS OUT, ANSWER FOR ME.

AND THE BOY-MONK TIPTOED OUT OF THE BACK DOOR AND RAN OFF LIKE THE WIND...

...WHILE THE MOUNTAIN WITCH WAITED.
HURRY UP! HAVEN'T YOU FINISHED?

WAIT A LITTLE, WAIT A LITTLE!

THE MOUNTAIN WITCH WAITED AND WAITED.
HOW LONG YOU TAKE. COME OUT, NOW!
WAIT A LITTLE, JUST A LITTLE...

AT LAST, SHE GOT TIRED OF WAITING AND KICKED OPEN THE DOOR.
WHAT! HE'S GONE!

I'VE BEEN TRICK-ED! I'VE BEEN TRICKED!

BUT I'LL CATCH YOU STILL.

THE WITCH SOON CAUGHT UP WITH THE BOY-MONK, BUT HE BROUGHT OUT ANOTHER GOOD-LUCK CHARM.
BE A HIGH SAND MOUNTAIN.

WHOOSH
WHOOSH

UP THE SAND MOUNTAIN WENT THE WITCH. SHE SLIPPED AND SANK, SANK AND SHOUTED...

...BUT FINALLY REACHED THE TOP.
WAIT, WAIT... I AM GOING TO EAT YOU UP!

THE BOY-MONK RAN ON AND ON AND WHEN HE COULD SEE THE MONASTERY IN THE DISTANCE HE FLUNG UP HIS LAST CHARM.
BE A BIG RIVER!

SPLASH
WHOOSH

THE WITCH TRIED TO SWIM AS FAST AS SHE COULD, BUT THE WAVES PUSHED HER BACK...
SLISH, SLOSH, SLISH, SLOSH.

...TILL THE BOY-MONK REACHED THE MONASTERY.
SAVE ME, SIR! SAVE ME. THE MOUNTAIN WITCH IS AFTER ME!

QUICK! GET INTO THE CUPBOARD.

SOON —
WHERE IS THAT MISERABLE BOY? I'LL EAT HIM FOR BREAKFAST.

OH, THE BOY-MONK? HE WENT OFF TO PICK CHESTNUTS YESTER-DAY. HE HASN'T COME BACK YET.
LIES! LIES! TELL ME WHERE HE IS!

I TOLD YOU, HE'S NOT HERE...! ARA! MY RICE-CAKES ARE BURNING.
RICE-CAKES! UMM!

THE WITCH'S HUGE NOSE TWITCHED GREEDILY.
SNIFF, SNIFF,
SNIFF, SNIFF.
I LOVE RICE CAKES. GIVE ME ONE, OLD MONK.

I'LL GIVE YOU AS MANY AS YOU WANT, BUT FIRST YOU MUST LET ME TEST YOUR MAGIC POWERS.
ANYTHING! ASK ME TO DO ANYTHING!

ALL RIGHT, THEN, HOW BIG...

...BIG...

...BIG...

...BIG CAN YOU BE? THIS I WANT TO SEE. THIS I WANT TO SEE.
WOOOZ

THE WITCH GREW SO TALL THAT SHE TOUCHED THE SKY.

GOOD, GOOD! NOW SHOW ME HOW SMALL...

...SMALL...SMALL YOU CAN BE. THIS I WANT TO SEE, THIS I WANT TO SEE.

ZOOM

THE WITCH SHRANK TILL SHE WAS NO HIGHER THAN THE FIRE TONGS.
CAN YOU GET ANY SMALLER?

THE WITCH SHRANK FURTHER.
AH, HA! YOU ARE NOW AS SMALL AS A SOYA-BEAN.

THE OLD MONK QUICKLY PUT THE WITCH BETWEEN TWO GOLDEN RICE-CAKES...

...AND POPPED THEM INTO HIS MOUTH.
AND THAT WAS THE END OF THE MOUNTAIN WITCH.

TO THIS DAY, VILLAGE CHILDREN IN JAPAN, SING A SONG WHILE PICKING CHESTNUTS.
THE MOUNTAIN WITCH IS DEAD AND GONE. SO NOW WE MAY GATHER CHESTNUTS HAPPILY, THIS LOVELY AUTUMN DAY.
CRISP AND JUICY CHESTNUTS, GO CRUNCH! CRUNCH! CRUNCH! THE WISE, OLD MONK HAS GOBBLED UP THE MOUNTAIN WITCH FOR LUNCH.

THE MAGIC SLIPPER

Story retold by Hema Pande
Illustrations: Ram Waeerkar

SUDDENLY—
WHAT ARE YOU DOING HERE, LITTLE ONE?

BEFORE KENTARO STOOD AN OLD MAN.
MY MOTHER IS ILL AND I HAVE NO MONEY TO... TO TAKE CARE OF HER.

IF I DON'T BUY HER SOME MEDICINE SOON... SHE WILL SURELY DIE.
DON'T WEEP, I'LL HELP YOU.

TAKE THIS WOODEN SLIPPER. WHEN YOU PUT IT ON AND JUMP, A GOLD COIN WILL FALL OUT OF IT.

BUT REMEMBER, NEVER TAKE OUT MORE THAN ONE COIN AT A TIME BECAUSE...

...EACH TIME YOU JUMP, YOU WILL SHRINK A LITTLE. AFTER A REST, YOU WILL BE YOURSELF AGAIN.

BUT TAKE OUT TOO MANY COINS AT ONCE AND YOU'LL BECOME AS TINY AS A MOSQUITO.

THE NEXT MOMENT THE OLD MAN VANISHED AND KENTARO AWOKE WITH A START.
WAS...WAS I DREAMING? BUT NO—THE WOODEN SLIPPER IS HERE!

I'LL GO HOME AND TRY IT OUT.

AS SOON AS HE REACHED THE COURTYARD OF HIS HOME HE PUT ON THE SLIPPER...

...AND JUMPED.
OH...!
RAP

A GOLD COIN DID FALL OUT! HOW HAPPY I AM! I CAN NOW BUY RICE, MEDICINES, ANYTHING, FOR MOTHER. SHE WILL BE WELL AGAIN.

THE WHOLE VILLAGE CAME TO KNOW OF KENTARO'S MAGIC SLIPPER AND EVERYONE WAS HAPPY FOR HIM. BUT NOT HIS UNCLE!
I MUST GET THAT SLIPPER FOR MYSELF! NOW!

HE WENT TO KENTARO'S HOUSE.
GOOD DAY, GOOD DAY, MY NEPHEW!
WELCOME, UNCLE.

KENTARO AND HIS MOTHER GAVE HIM A DELICIOUS MEAL.
EXCELLENT FOOD! AH! UM ··· AHEM ··· I HEAR YOU HAVE A MAGIC SLIPPER THAT GIVES GOLD COINS.
I DO, UNCLE. I'LL SHOW IT TO YOU.

THIS IS THE SLIPPER, UNCLE!
WILL YOU SELL IT TO ME? I'LL PAY YOU ANYTHING YOU WANT.

HEH—HEH! LET'S ALSO FORGET ABOUT ALL THE MONEY YOU OWE ME. WHAT DO YOU SAY, EH?
THIS SLIPPER WAS GIVEN TO ME BY A KIND, OLD MAN. I CANNOT SELL IT TO YOU.

THEN AT LEAST LEND IT TO ME FOR A DAY.
NO! NO, UNCLE! I CANNOT.

OH, COME NOW...

JUST FOR A DAY, NEPHEW. I'LL RETURN IT TOMORROW.
UNCLE! WAIT!

THE UNCLE HURRIED HOME. HE SPREAD A MAT ON THE GRASS IN HIS INNER YARD.
WILL IT REALLY WORK?

I CAN'T BELIEVE IT!
RAP

HE JUMPED AGAIN.

BEAUTIFUL, SHINING, LOVELY, GOLD COINS!
BESIDE HIMSELF WITH JOY, THE UNCLE JUMPED AND JUMPED ...
RAP
RAP
RAP
RAP

... TILL SOON, A PILE OF GOLD COINS LAY ON THE MAT.
HO HO HO! I'LL BE THE RICHEST MAN IN JAPAN.

I'M TIRED. I'LL REST FOR A WHILE, THEN START ALL OVER AGAIN.

SUDDENLY—
WHAT'S THIS? THAT GOLD COIN... IT LOOKS AS BIG AS A MAT!

WHY, NOW! THIS PILE LOOKS LIKE A MOUNTAIN OF GOLD! IT'S HIGHER THAN FUJIYAMA!

FRIGHTENED, HE LOOKED ALL AROUND HIM.
THE TREES ARE TOUCHING THE SKY! GOOD HEAVENS! WHAT IS HAPPENING?

I CANNOT SEE THE END OF MY GARDEN! THE HOUSE LOOKS GIGANTIC!

JUST THEN, KENTARO ARRIVED THERE. HE LOOKED FOR HIS UNCLE ALL OVER THE HOUSE, THEN AT LAST, IN THE INNER YARD—
WHAT A PILE OF COINS!

BUT WHERE HAS UNCLE GONE?

UNCLE, UNCLE... WHERE ARE YOU?

THEN A THOUGHT STRUCK KENTARO.
COULD IT BE THAT UNCLE, BY TAKING OUT ALL THESE GOLD COINS, HAS NOW BECOME AS TINY AS A MOSQUITO? IS THAT WHY I CAN'T SEE HIM?

WHAT'S THIS ON THE SLIPPER? IT LOOKS LIKE A LITTLE BEETLE...

UNCLE — YOU! OH, NO! HOW TERRIBLE!

HELP ME! SAVE ME! DO SOMETHING!

BUT KENTARO COULD NOT EVEN HEAR HIS UNCLE'S SHOUTS.
POOR UNCLE! I CAN DO NOTHING TO HELP HIM. HIS GREED HAS BROUGHT HIM TO THIS SORRY STATE.

KENTARO PUT THE HEAP OF GOLD COINS INTO A BAG AND WENT HOME AND HE AND HIS MOTHER LIVED HAPPILY EVER AFTER.

THE GRATEFUL CRANE
Script: Vaijayanti Wagle
Illustrations: Ashok Dongre
LATE ONE WINTER EVENING, KEIJI WAS ON HIS WAY HOME, WHEN—
HUH? WHAT IS THAT AHEAD?

A WOUNDED CRANE! WHO COULD HAVE BEEN SO CRUEL?

YOU ARE HURT. DON'T WORRY, I WILL HELP YOU.

NOW KEEP STILL WHILE I REMOVE THIS ARROW.

YOU ARE LUCKY. YOUR FEATHERS HAVE PROTECTED YOU.

THE CRANE STOOD UP AND BOWED LOW.
NO! NO! DO NOT THANK ME. YOU ARE A BEAUTIFUL BIRD. I WAS GLAD TO HELP.

WITH A FLUTTER OF ITS WINGS THE CRANE FLEW AWAY INTO THE AIR AND THEN KEIJI RETURNED HOME.

DAYS PASSED. ONE DAY, WHILE KEIJI AND HIS FATHER WERE WORKING IN THE FIELDS, A LOST YOUNG ORPHAN GIRL ARRIVED AT THEIR HOUSE.
KIND LADY, CAN YOU TELL ME THE PATH OUT OF THESE WOODS?
WHY, CERTAINLY, MY CHILD.

BUT YOU LOOK TIRED. SPEND THE NIGHT HERE. TOMORROW YOU CAN CONTINUE YOUR JOURNEY, REFRESHED.
THAT WOULD BE VERY NICE, THANK YOU.

THROUGHOUT THE DAY THE GRATEFUL GIRL HELPED KEIJI'S OLD MOTHER IN THE HOUSE.
WHAT A NICE YOUNG GIRL.

IN THE EVENING KEIJI AND HIS FATHER RETURNED FROM THE FIELDS.
HMM, THE AROMA OF DELICIOUS FOOD FILLS THE AIR.
THANK OUR NEW GUEST, MIDORI. SHE HAS CLEANED THE HOUSE AND COOKED OUR DINNER.

SOON—
YOU HAVE BEEN SUCH A HELP TO MY MOTHER.
YES, MIDORI. WHY DON'T YOU STAY A WHILE LONGER?

DO STAY, MIDORI.
YOU ARE ALL SO KIND. I WILL STAY A WEEK LONGER.

BUT AT THE END OF THE WEEK—
WE HAVE GROWN FOND OF YOU. WON'T YOU MAKE YOUR HOME WITH US, DEAR CHILD?
OH, MAMASAN*! I TOO HAVE GROWN TO LOVE YOU DEARLY. I WILL BE HONOURED TO STAY WITH YOU!

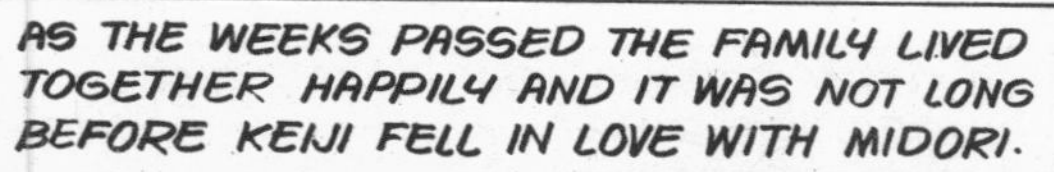
AS THE WEEKS PASSED THE FAMILY LIVED TOGETHER HAPPILY AND IT WAS NOT LONG BEFORE KEIJI FELL IN LOVE WITH MIDORI.

MIDORI! MIDORI! I HOPE YOU WILL MARRY ME.

BUT TROUBLED TIMES WERE AHEAD. ONE DAY—
ALAS, THE HARVEST HAS BEEN RUINED BY THE EARLY FROST. WE SHALL BE VERY POOR IN THE COMING MONTHS.

MIDORI WAS DEEPLY DISTRESSED.
HONOURABLE FATHER! I MUST LEAVE THEN, FOR I SHALL ONLY BE A BURDEN TO YOU.
NO! HOW CAN YOU SAY THAT?

PLEASE STAY!
YOU HAVE DONE SO MUCH FOR US.
WELL, THEN I WILL. BUT YOU MUST LET ME HELP YOU...

* MOTHER DEAR

... I WILL WEAVE A LENGTH OF BROCADE. SELL IT AND YOU WILL HAVE ENOUGH MONEY TO BUY FOOD FOR THE ENTIRE WINTER.
THEN I'LL GO AND BRING YOU FINE SILK THREAD.

NO, NO! I HAVE ALL I NEED. I ONLY ASK TO BE LEFT COMPLETELY ALONE FOR THREE DAYS AND THREE NIGHTS.

BUT... HOW WILL YOU EAT?
LEAVE A BOWL OF RICE AND A PIECE OF RADISH EVERY NIGHT OUTSIDE MY DOOR.

SO EVERY EVENING KEIJI PLACED FOOD OUTSIDE THE DOOR...
...AND EACH MORNING, HE TOOK BACK AN EMPTY BOWL.

ON THE FOURTH DAY THE DOOR SLID OPEN AND MIDORI EMERGED.
OH! OH! WHAT BEAUTIFUL BROCADE!
IT'S EXQUISITE!

AT THE MARKET, MERCHANTS VIED WITH ONE ANOTHER TO BUY THE BROCADE.
I WILL OFFER YOU 20 GOLD COINS.
I'LL GIVE YOU 30!
HERE'S 50!

THAT EVENING KEIJI CAME HOME WITH A BAG FULL OF GOLD COINS.

WHEN SPRING CAME, MIDORI DECIDED TO WEAVE ANOTHER LENGTH OF BROCADE.

THE FAMILY PROMISED NOT TO DISTURB HER AS MIDORI SHUT HERSELF IN A ROOM.

EVERY EVENING KEIJI PLACED A BOWL OF RICE AND RADISH OUTSIDE MIDORI'S DOOR.

TREMBLING WITH EXCITEMENT, KEIJI SLID THE DOOR OPEN.
FORGIVE ME FOR DISTURBING YOU, BUT...I...

THERE WAS A FLUTTER OF WINGS AND...
WHERE IS MY MIDORI? WHO ARE YOU?

I AM THE CRANE YOU RESCUED LONG AGO. I TOOK THE FORM OF A WOMAN TO THANK YOU FOR YOUR GREAT KINDNESS.
BUT...BUT...

AH, KEIJI! HAD YOU BUT KEPT YOUR PROMISE AND NOT DISTURBED ME, I WOULD HAVE GIVEN UP BEING A CRANE FOREVER!
OH, BUT DO FORGIVE ME!

WE WOULD HAVE GOT MARRIED. FOR I KNOW YOU LOVE ME DEARLY AND I TOO HAVE GROWN TO LOVE YOU...
OH, MIDORI!

...BUT NOW THAT CANNOT BE. THE SPELL IS BROKEN...

SELL THIS BROCADE AND YOU AND YOUR FAMILY WILL NEVER BE IN NEED AGAIN.

THE CRANE STEPPED OUT OF THE HOUSE, LIFTED ITS WINGS...
KEIJI... YOU AND I WILL NEVER MEET AGAIN...

... AND ROSE INTO THE SKY —

THROUGH HIS TEARS KEIJI WATCHED IT CIRCLE HIGHER AND HIGHER TILL IT VANISHED.

SADLY, KEIJI TUCKED ONE FEATHER INTO HIS SASH IN MEMORY OF HIS BELOVED MIDORI AND THE CRANE WHO HAD THE GRACE TO SAY THANK YOU.

THE MEANIHOS

Based on a story sent by :
Rashmi R. Menon

OH SURE! WHY NOT?

ZOOM
ZIP
PLOP

HURRAH! WE'RE SAVED. I'LL LEAVE THEM IN THE ABANDONED MILL.

HANAHITO'S FORTUNE CHANGED AND IT SURPRISED HIS JEALOUS NEIGHBOUR, JOBHIHO.
TILL YESTERDAY HE WAS A PAUPER. TODAY HIS GRANARY IS OVERFLOWING!
IT'S BECAUSE THEY'VE GOT RID OF THE MEANIHOS IN THEIR HOUSE.
OH... I SEE ... AHEM.

JOBHIHO MADE HIS WAY TO THE ABANDONED MILL.
YOU POOR THINGS, LET ME FREE YOU AT ONCE.
WHAT A NICE MAN.
WHEW! IT WAS GETTING A BIT CRAMPED IN HERE.

NOW YOU CAN GO BACK TO HANAHITO. HEE! HEE!
NEVER! HE'S SUCH A CRUEL MAN.
WE'LL STAY WITH YOU!

AND THE MEANIHOS MADE THEMSELVES COMFORTABLE IN JOBHIHO'S FARM.
WHAT HAVE I DONE? I'M RUINED!

THE WOODEN SHOES

* WOODEN SHOES

WHEN HE CAME TO, HEYSHIRO WAS FILLED WITH RAGE.
I'LL TAKE REVENGE ONE DAY, NO MATTER HOW LONG IT TAKES.

HE PLANNED AND PLOTTED FOR DAYS. AT LAST—
OUR EMPEROR MIKADO HAS A HIGH REGARD FOR LEARNED MONKS. I MUST BECOME A MONK AND WIN THE EMPEROR'S FAVOUR AND HAVE KING MASAMU PUNISHED.

HEYSHIRO ENROLLED AS A MONK IN A BUDDHIST MONASTERY—

AS THE YEARS ROLLED BY HEYSHIRO BECAME A LEARNED PRIEST WHOSE FAME SPREAD OVER THE COUNTRY.

ONE DAY, EMPEROR MIKADO FELL SERIOUSLY ILL. THE MINISTERS CALLED FOR PRIESTS AND MONKS TO TRY FAITH HEALING.
IT'S NO USE. NO ONE SEEMS TO BE OF ANY HELP.

HEYSHIRO TOO WAS SENT FOR—
I CAN'T CURE HIM. ALL I CAN DO IS PRAY FOR HIM.

LUCKILY FOR HEYSHIRO, THE EMPEROR RECOVERED. HEYSHIRO'S FAME SPREAD FAR AND WIDE. A SPECIAL MONASTERY WAS BUILT FOR HIM NEAR THE PALACE.
THE TIME HAS NOW COME FOR REVENGE.

AS HIS THOUGHTS DWELT ON REVENGE, A STRANGE LIGHT FILLED THE ROOM.

WHAT AN UNUSUAL SIGHT! A HEAVENLY AURA SEEMS TO BE SPREADING AROUND ME.

THE BURNING DESIRE FOR REVENGE WHICH HE HAD NURSED IN HIS HEART FOR YEARS WAS SUDDENLY QUELLED.
AT LAST! I FEEL AT PEACE.

THE NEXT DAY, HE SENT FOR KING MASAMU, WHO CAME EAGERLY TO MEET THE RENOWNED MONK.
I AM HONOURED THAT YOU CALLED ME.

ON A SMALL PEDESTAL BEFORE THE MONK LAY THE PAIR OF WOODEN SHOES WITH WHICH MASAMU HAD HIT HEYSHIRO.
DO YOU RECOGNI E THESE?
NO!

HEYSHIRO RELATED THE EVENTS OF THE PAST.
FORGIVE ME, WISE MONK. I WAS YOUNG AND ARROGANT THEN!
TO ERR IS HUMAN! WE ALL MAKE MISTAKES.

HEYSHIRO LIFTED THE KING WITH AN AFFECTIONATE EMBRACE.
TODAY I HAVE REALISED HOW BITTER IT MAKES A MAN TO HARBOUR RANCOUR IN HIS HEART. LET US BOTH FORGIVE AND FORGET THE PAST.

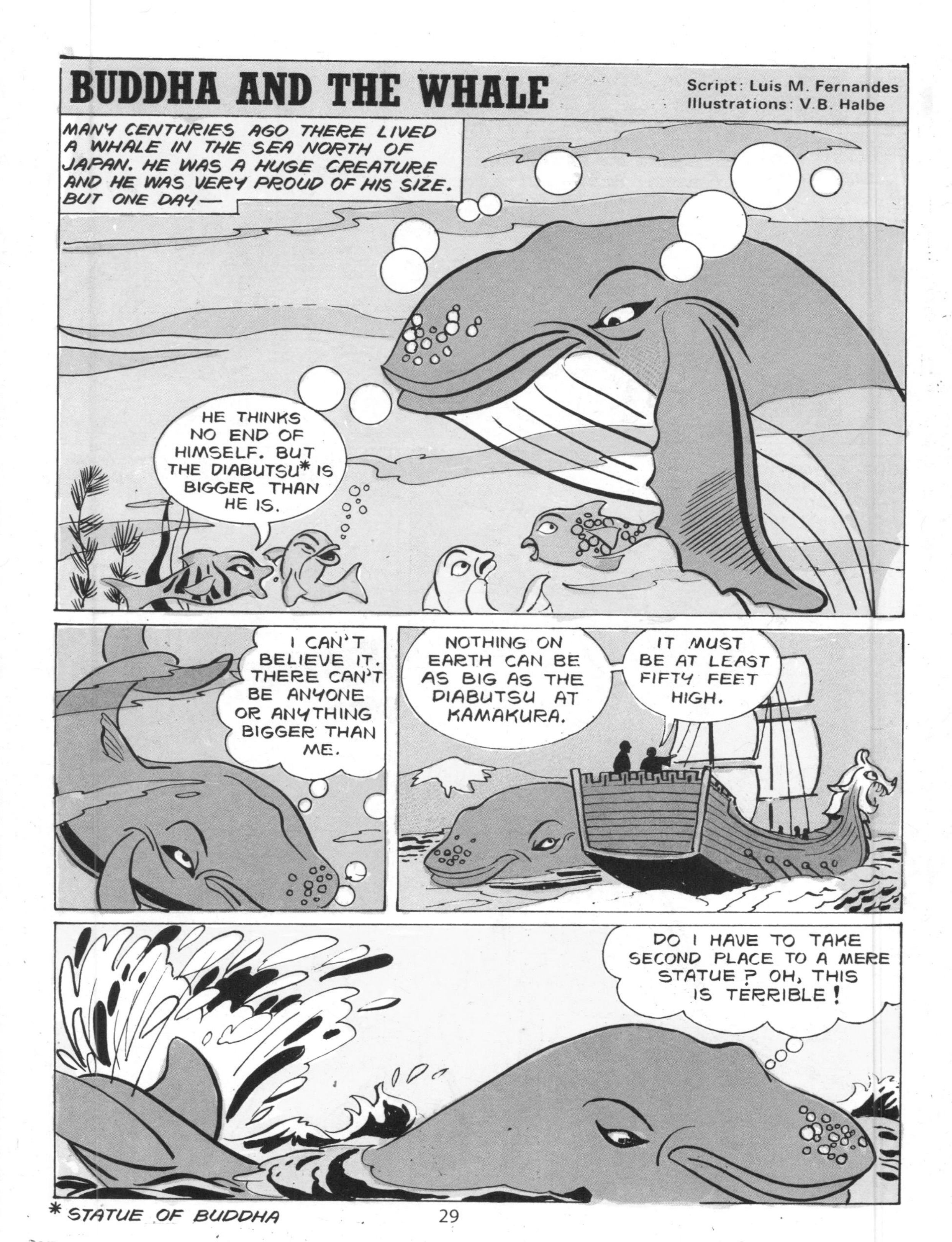

* STATUE OF BUDDHA

JUST THEN HE MET HIS FRIEND, THE SHARK.
WHY ARE YOU LOOKING SO GLOOMY?
THEY SAY THERE IS A STATUE OF BUDDHA AT KAMAKURA WHICH IS BIGGER THAN I AM.
THAT CAN'T BE TRUE.

BUT IF YOU WISH I WILL GO TO KAMAKURA AND GET THE EXACT MEASUREMENTS OF THAT IMAGE.
THAT IS VERY KIND OF YOU.

The Shark SET OUT. WHEN HE REACHEDT HE COAST OF JAPAN—
I CAN'T GO ANY FURTHER.

FRIEND RAT!

YES?
MY FRIEND, THE WHALE, WANTS TO KNOW HOW BIG THE DIABUTSU IS.

COULD YOU PLEASE GET ME THE EXACT MEASUREMENTS OF THE STATUE ?
WAIT HERE.

THE RAT SCURRIED OFF TO THE STATUE...

...AND WENT ROUND THE IMAGE COUNTING HIS STEPS AS HE DID SO.
...THREE THOUSAND NINE HUNDRED AND NINETY-NINE...

THEN HE RETURNED TO THE SHARK.
I HAD TO TAKE FIVE THOUSAND STEPS TO GO ROUND THE STATUE.
IS IT SO HUGE ?

THE SHARK RETURNED HOME AND TOLD THE WHALE WHAT HE HAD LEARNT.
FIVE THOUSAND STEPS TO GO ROUND THE STATUE ? IT MUST BE VERY BIG INDEED.
YES.

BUT IS IT BIGGER THAN ME I MUST SEE THAT STATUE FOR MYSELF.

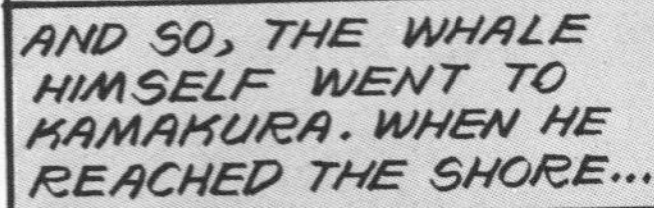
AND SO, THE WHALE HIMSELF WENT TO KAMAKURA. WHEN HE REACHED THE SHORE...

...HE PUT ON MAGICAL SLIPPERS...
... AND WALKED TO THE STATUE.

BUT WHEN HE TRIED TO ENTER THE GATE—
I'M STUCK.

WHAT ARE YOU TRYING TO DO!
I HAVE COME TO SEE THE DIABUTSU. I DEMAND TO KNOW HOW BIG IT IS.

SUDDENLY, THE DIABUTSU ITSELF GOT TO ITS FEET.

THE PRIEST MEASURED THE STATUE WITH THE HELP OF HIS ROSARY.

AND THEN HE MEASURED THE WHALE IN THE SAME WAY. WHEN HE HAD FINISHED—

THE DIABUTSU IS A FINGER SHORTER THAN YOU.

I KNEW IT!

THE DIABUTSU RETURNED TO ITS SITTING POSTURE. AND THE WHALE RETURNED HOME, FEELING VERY HAPPY.

THE STORY OF THE WHALE IS A FANTASY BUT THE STATUE OF BUDDHA AT KAMAKURA IS VERY REAL. THE CENTURIES-OLD STATUE IS MADE OF BRONZE AND IS OVER THIRTEEN METRES IN HEIGHT.

ISSUNBOSHI
Script:
Gayatri Madan Dutt
Illustrations:
Ram Waeerkar

IN THE VILLAGE OF SUMIYOSHI, THERE ONCE LIVED A POOR COUPLE.
AH, WIFE - IF ONLY WE HAD A CHILD TO BRING LIGHT TO OUR LIVES!
YES, HUSBAND. EVERY NIGHT, I PRAY FOR A LITTLE BOY; JUST ONE LITTLE BOY!

AND SOON, THE PRAYER WAS ANSWERED. THEIR "LITTLE BOY" WAS BORN, AND OH, HOW LITTLE HE WAS ...
... HE'S SO TINY!
BUT WE'LL LOVE HIM JUST THE SAME — OUR LITTLE ISSUNBOSHI!

ISSUNBOSHI GREW UP, BUT HE DIDN'T GROW ANY BIGGER IN SIZE, AND ONE DAY —
MOTHER, I FEEL SO USELESS! I AM TOO SMALL EITHER TO HELP YOU AROUND THE HOUSE, OR FATHER IN THE FIELDS.

PLEASE LET ME GO OUT AND LOOK FOR A JOB WHERE I WILL FIT IN PERFECTLY, DESPITE MY SIZE. KYOTO — THAT IS MY DESTINATION!
MY SON, WILL IT NOT BE DANGEROUS FOR ONE SO SMALL AS YOU TO GO OUT INTO THE WORLD?
BUT THOUGH THEY WERE AFRAID FOR HIM, HIS PARENTS DID NOT WANT TO STAND IN THE WAY OF ISSUNBOSHI FINDING AN INDEPENDENT LIFE FOR HIMSELF...

...SO THE NEXT DAY, THEY TOOK HIM DOWN TO THE RIVER, AND PRESENTED HIM WITH THREE GIFTS FOR HIS JOURNEY — A SOUP-BOWL, A CHOPSTICK AND A NEEDLE...
...A BOAT, AN OAR AND A SWORD — OH, THANK YOU, DEAR PARENTS.

AND ISSUNBOSHI BEGAN HIS JOURNEY UPSTREAM TO KYOTO.
IT WAS HARD WORK FOR A TINY FELLOW, BUT THAT DID NOT DETER HIM.

IT HAD GROWN DARK. SUDDENLY, A FISH CAME UP TO THE SURFACE FOR AIR — RIGHT UNDER ISSUNBOSHI'S BOAT, AND —
BLOOP-OOP-OOP-OOK
SPLASH

HELP ! HELP !
AND ISSUNBOSHI CLUNG DESPERATELY TO HIS OVERTURNED SOUP-BOWL.

JUST THEN, SOME LIGHTS APPEARED FROM DOWN-STREAM. IT WAS THE ROYAL FLOTILLA.

IN ONE OF THE BOATS SAT A BEAUTIFUL PRINCESS. AS SHE LOOKED OUT OVER THE WATER —
WHAT IS THAT STRANGE THING FLOATING THERE...?

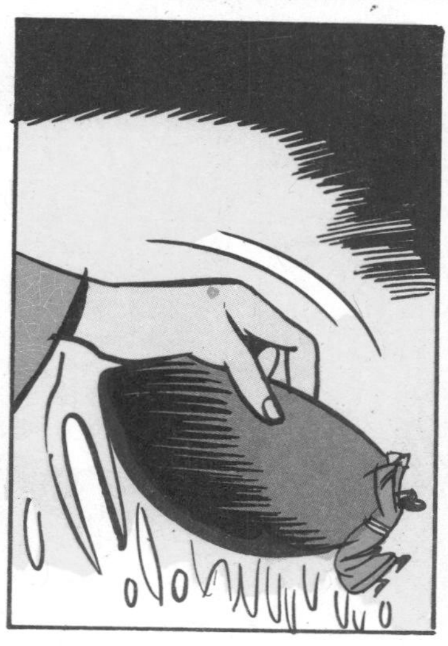

SAVED !

OH — IT'S JUST A SOUP-BOWL...
I'LL HIDE AMONG THESE SILK CUSHIONS.

SOON, THE BOATS DOCKED — AT KYOTO !
THE TRAVELLERS GOT OFF AND SO DID ISSUNBOSHI.

HE FOLLOWED THEIR FOOTPRINTS, TILL HE CAME TO HUGE, DECORATED GATES. IT WAS THE PALACE!
OY! HOY! AHOY! PICK ME UP, YOU CHATTERING GUARDS!

BUT THE GUARDS CHATTED ON. THEY HADN'T EVEN HEARD HIM!
THEN ISSUNBOSHI HAD AN IDEA...

... FOR, SUDDENLY —
?
?
TIP TAP
TIP TAP

HUH...? A SLIPPER DANCING ALL BY ITSELF?
TIP TAP
TIP TAP

A GUARD BENT DOWN TO INVESTIGATE.
LOOK OUT, OR YOU'LL SQUASH ME!
OH-OH! WHAT DO WE HAVE HERE?

HEY, HEY— WILL YOU LOOK AT THIS? IT'S A PEA-SIZED SAMURAI!
NO— I'M A REAL SAMURAI!

TAKE ME TO YOUR LORD. I SEEK A POSI- TION WITH HIM.
HA, HA, HA!
HO, HO, HO! COME ALONG THEN!

AND SOON THERE WAS ISSUNBOSHI BEFORE THE GREAT LORD HIMSELF.
WHY, IT'S THE LITTLEST MAN I HAVE EVER SEEN!
BUT A BRAVE ONE, SIRE! I HAVE COME TO KYOTO IN THE TEETH OF GREAT DANGERS, BUT IN YOUR SERVICE I AM PREPARED TO FACE EVEN GREATER DANGERS!

VALOROUSLY SPOKEN! I APPOINT YOU PERSONAL GUARD OVER MY YOUNG DAUGHTER, THE PRINCESS.
I WILL GUARD HER WITH MY LIFE!

HOW DELIGHTED THE PRINCESS WAS WITH HER NEW BODYGUARD WHOSE LIFE SHE DIDN'T KNOW SHE HAD SAVED! THE TWO BECAME GOOD FRIENDS.
HERE, ISSUN—MY FAVOURITE RICE-CAKE. HOW CAN I EAT IT WITHOUT FIRST GIVING SOME TO YOU?
THANK YOU MY PRINCESS.

AND, OF COURSE, ISSUNBOSHI DID HIS BEST TO BE USEFUL! WHEN THE PRINCESS'S KIMONO GOT A TINY TEAR IN IT—
THERE! I'VE DARNED IT PERFECTLY WITH MY "SWORD!"

AND IF A MOSQUITO DARED TO COME NEAR HIS BELOVED PRINCESS—
AAA-YA-EEE...

AND THAT WAS THE END OF THE MOSQUITO!
ZUK

SOON ONE DAY, NEWS SPREAD THROUGH THE PALACE THAT THE GREAT LORD WAS GOING TO CHOOSE A HUSBAND FOR HIS DAUGHTER.
ISSUN—TO PRAY THAT MY HUSBAND BE A GOOD MAN, I WANT TO GO TO THE DISTANT SHRINE OF THE BLESSING BUDDHA.
I WILL GO WITH YOU—RIDING IN YOUR KIMONO SLEEVE.

SO THEY SET OUT ALONG THE AVENUES OF CHERRY BLOSSOMS... BUT THEY HAD BARELY REACHED THE SHRINE THAN —
AAAARGH! AAAA! OOAA...
IT WAS THE GIANT GREEN-OGRE, FEARED THROUGHOUT THE LAND.

AHA! YOU'LL MAKE A TASTY SNACK, PRINCESS!

BUT THAT WAS SOONER SPOKEN THAN DONE, FOR —
AAA-YAA-EEE...
SWOOSH!

EAT MY PRINCESS, WILL YOU? MY SWORD WILL EAT YOU!
JIB JAB PIK POKE
AAOW! WHAT'S THAT?
AND SETTING ASIDE THE PRINCESS...

...THE OGRE CLUTCHED AT HIS NOSE. THE IMPACT OF HIS HAND MADE ISSUN-BOSHI LOSE HIS GRIP, AND —
PLOP!
THE OGRE SWALLOWED HARD...

...AND DOWN WENT ISSUN-BOSHI INTO THE GREEN DARKNESS OF THE OGRE'S STOMACH.
UGH!
BUT HE DID NOT LOSE HIS PRESENCE OF MIND...

...FOR THE NEXT MOMENT —
OOOH! AAAH! MY STOMACH...
PIK PIK
JIB JAB

...AND TO THE OGRE'S EARS CAME A DEEP VOICE AMPLIFIED THROUGH HAVING TRAVELLED UP HIS FOOD-PIPE!
LET THE PRINCESS GO, DO YOU HEAR?
LET HER GO AT ONCE!

I CERTAINLY WON'T!
THEN I'LL JAB YOU EVEN HARDER!
JABBITY JAB JA-A-AB!

OW! OOOH! STOP!... WHOEVER... WHATEVER YOU ARE... I'LL LET THE PRINCESS GO, BUT I BEG YOU, COME OUT OF THERE!
ALL RIGHT — COUGH THEN!

THE OGRE GAVE A RESOUNDING COUGH, AND...
ZWOOOP!
...OUT FLEW ISSUNBOSHI!

THE OGRE PEERED DOWN AND WAS AMAZED.
A TINY FELLOW LIKE YOU INFLICTING SUCH PAIN? LIKE YOUR COUSINS, THE BUGS AND THE BEETLES, YOU TOO ARE A TROUBLESOME CREATURE!

NOW THAT REALLY "BUGGED" ISSUNBOSHI!
GET OUT OF HERE, YOU CAD, BEFORE I MAKE MORE TROUBLE FOR YOU!
I... I'M GOING... HAVING MET YOU, I'LL NEVER COME NEAR HUMAN HABITATION AGAIN.
AND THE OGRE WENT OFF INTO THE MOUNTAINS TO MEDITATE.

MEANWHILE, THE PRINCESS HAD BEEN GAZING UNBELIEVINGLY AT ISSUNBOSHI.
ISSUN, YOU HAVE SAVED ME, NOT FROM A MOSQUITO THIS TIME, BUT THE GIANT GREEN-OGRE HIMSELF!
PRINCESS, I... HEY, WHAT'S THAT?

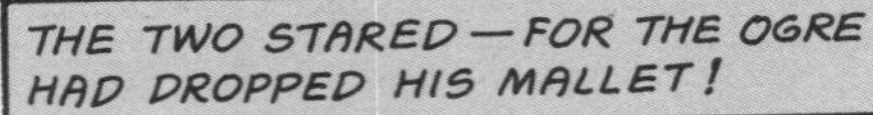
THE TWO STARED — FOR THE OGRE HAD DROPPED HIS MALLET!

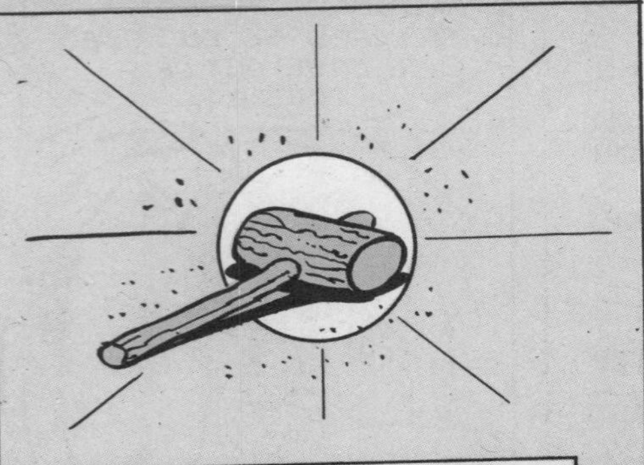
THERE IT LAY, THE FAMOUS MAGIC MALLET. TOUCH IT, MAKE A WISH, AND IT COMES TRUE!

NOW ISSUNBOSHI AND THE PRINCESS HAD JUST ONE WISH. SO THEY TOUCHED IT, CLOSED THEIR EYES AND WISHED HARD!

THE NEXT INSTANT—
ZOO...OOM...OOM...OOM...OOOM!
ISSUNBOSHI GREW — TALLER AND TALLER, TILL...

...THERE HE STOOD, A NORMAL, HANDSOME YOUNG MAN.
DEAR, ISSUN...
DEAR, PRINCESS...

AND WHEN THE WHOLE STORY AND ISSUNBOSHI'S BRAVE PART IN IT WAS TOLD TO THE GREAT LORD, HE WAS ONLY TOO HAPPY TO GIVE THEM HIS BLESSINGS. AND SOON AMID MUCH POMP AND GRANDEUR, ISSUNBOSHI AND THE PRINCESS WERE MARRIED.

ISSUNBOSHI INVITED HIS PARENTS TO COME AND LIVE WITH THEM, AND WHEN THEY COULD NOT BELIEVE THAT HE WAS REALLY THEIR SON, SHOWED THEM THE "NEEDLE-SWORD" THE ONLY ONE REMAINING OF THE THREE GIFTS THEY HAD ONCE GIVEN THEIR "LITTLE" BOY!

THE CLAY WARRIORS

Based on a story sent by:
Sunjeetha Balu

Illustrations:
Chandu

HE HASTILY SUMMONED TAKAGI TOU —
THE THIRD DAY AFTER THE FULL MOON IS JUST TWO DAYS AWAY. YOU MUST PREPARE TO DEFEND US.
BUT WE NEED NEW WEAPONS, MY LORD.

YOU MUST THINK OF A PLAN WITHIN TWO DAYS, ELSE, WE ARE DOOMED.

TAKAGI TOU THOUGHT AND THOUGHT AND FINALLY—
SIRE, I HAVE A PLAN. THIS IS WHAT WE WILL DO...

EXCELLENT. BEGIN THE PREPARA-TIONS AT ONCE.

SOON—
LET THE POTTERS BEGIN THEIR WORK. I WANT EVERYTHING FINISHED BEFORE NIGHTFALL.

MEANWHILE, IN THE ENEMY CAMP—
MY LORD, OUR SPIES REPORT THAT THERE IS MUCH ACTIVITY HAPPENING IN THE PALACE BUT NO ONE KNOWS WHAT THEY ARE PLANNING.
HA! WHAT CAN THEY DO NOW? WE'LL SURELY DEFEAT THEM.

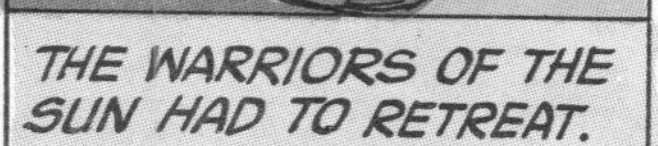

I DECLARE YOU MY CHIEF ADVISER. FROM TODAY YOU WILL ADVISE ME ON ALL MATTERS RELATING TO THE STATE.

I AM HONOURED, MY LORD.

SHINI'S MAGIC NEEDLE

Story : Dnyandev Chaudhary
Script : Priya Khanna
Illustrations : Chandu

THAT NIGHT AS SHE LAY AWAKE IN HER LITTLE COTTAGE —

DON'T BE SAD, SHINI.

?!

SUDDENLY, A BRIGHT LIGHT FILLED THE ROOM AND A FAIRY APPEARED.

YOU ARE A GOOD GIRL. I HAVE BROUGHT YOU SOME CLOTH, THREADS AND A MAGIC NEEDLE.

ARE YOU FOR REAL, FAIRY?

NO SOONER HAD SHE EMBROIDERED THE FISH THAN...
?
...THE FISH LEAPT OUT OF THE CLOTH...

...AND JUMPED INTO A DRUM OF WATER.
UNBELIEVABLE! THE FISH HAS COME TO LIFE. THIS IS A MAGIC NEEDLE!
SPLASH

SHINI PUT HER MAGIC NEEDLE TO GOOD USE.
I'LL QUICKLY EMBROIDER A DOLL FOR THE CHILD TILL HER MOTHER RETURNS.
WAAAH
THE DOLL EMERGED FROM THE CLOTH AND THE CHILD STOPPED CRYING.

SOON THE ENTIRE VILLAGE KNEW ABOUT SHINI'S MAGIC NEEDLE.
I'LL ASK THAT GIRL TO MAKE LOTS OF JEWELS AND FINE CLOTHES FOR ME.
IT WAS THE GREEDY WIFE OF THE VILLAGE CHIEF.

BUT—
I WILL NOT MAKE ANYTHING FOR YOU. YOU ARE BEING GREEDY.
IMPERTINENT GIRL!

SHINI WAS LOCKED UP IN THE STORE-ROOM. AFTER THREE DAYS—
THAT GIRL WILL DO ANYTHING THAT I SAY. SHE MUST HAVE GROWN WEAK WITH HUNGER BY NOW.

BUT—
YOU WICKED GIRL! YOU'VE GOT THE MAGIC NEEDLE TO GIVE YOU FOOD. GIVE THAT NEEDLE TO ME!
I WILL NOT.

SHINI'S HANDS WERE BUSY EMBROIDERING A DEER WITH WINGS.
THE DEER CAME TO LIFE AND...
BYE BYE, GREEDY WOMAN!
...TOOK OFF, WITH SHINI ON ITS BACK.
STOP!
OH! SHE'S PELTING STONES AT US.
SHINI MADE A BOW AND ARROWS WITH THE MAGIC NEEDLE.
EEEEEEE! AN..A..RR..ROW!
THE CHIEF'S WIFE FAINTED WITH FRIGHT.
AFTER A LONG FLIGHT, SHINI DECIDED TO LAND.
I WONDER WHERE I AM.
YOU'VE COME FAR AWAY FROM YOUR VILLAGE, SHINI. GO AND MAKE A LIVING WITH YOUR MAGIC NEEDLE. BUT REMEMBER, YOU MUST MAKE INCOMPLETE FIGURES OTHERWISE EVERYTHING THAT YOU MAKE WILL COME TO LIFE.
SO SAYING, THE DEER DISAPPEARED.
SHINI FOLLOWED THE DEER'S ADVICE AND OPENED A LITTLE SHOP IN THE MARKET.
I'LL BUY THESE HANKIES.
THANKFULLY, SHE HASN'T NOTICED THAT THE BIRDS ON THOSE HANKIES HAVE A TOE MISSING.
HOWEVER, ONE DAY SHE EMBROIDERED A COMPLETE PEACOCK BY MISTAKE. SO—
EEEEE! A PEACOCK!
WHERE DID IT COME FROM?
SHINI'S MAGIC NEEDLE WAS NO LONGER A SECRET.

THE KING OF THE LAND HEARD ABOUT IT AND CALLED SHINI TO THE COURT.
EMBROIDER A GOLDEN GOOSE FOR ME.
I WILL NOT LET THEM MISUSE MY MAGIC NEEDLE.

SHINI MADE A HUGE BLACK CROW INSTEAD.
OH! SILLY GIRL! YOU DON'T EVEN KNOW WHAT A GOOSE LOOKS LIKE. ANYWAY, MAKE A GOLDEN DEER FOR ME.

SO —
HA! I'M SMARTER THAN YOU THINK. A DIRTY SMELLY PIG IS ALL THAT YOU'LL GET.
EEE! A PIG! LOCK THIS GIRL IN THE DUNGEON.
OINK
SHINI'S MAGIC NEEDLE WAS TAKEN AWAY.

THE GREEDY QUEEN SET TO WORK WITH THE MAGIC NEEDLE.
MOUNTAINS AND MOUNTAINS OF GOLD! WE'LL HAVE UNLIMITED WEALTH.
HA! HA!

BUT —
EEEE! BURNING COAL!
HELP! THE PALACE WILL CATCH FIRE.

THE MOUNTAINS SEEMED TO FOLLOW THEM.
AAAOWWW! HELP!
GET THAT GIRL FROM THE DUNGEON!

SO —
DON'T WORRY, MY LORD. THERE WILL SOON BE LOTS OF WATER TO PUT OUT THE FIRE.
NOW I CAN GET BACK AT THE HORRID KING AND HIS GREEDY QUEEN.

STREAMS AND STREAMS OF WATER GUSHED IN.
SWOOOOSHH

THE FIRE WAS PUT OUT, BUT—
GLUB
WE'LL .. GURGLE .. GLUB .. DROWN !
GLUB

SHINI MADE A BOAT ON THE CLOTH.
UGH .. GRUNT .. YOU ARE A GOOD GIRL.
HEH ! HEH ! NOW PLEASE GIVE US A LOT OF GOLD. WE'LL HAVE YOU AS OUR CHIEF COURTIER.
OH ! HE'LL NEVER LEARN A LESSON !

WOULD YOUR MAJESTY LIKE TO SAIL FOR A WHILE FIRST? MY MAGIC NEEDLE WILL GIVE THE BREEZE TO GET THE BOAT MOVING.
AH ! HOW LOVELY !
YES, WE'D LOVE TO SAIL.

SO, THE BOAT BEGAN TO SAIL. SHINI EMBROIDERED MORE WATER ON THE CLOTH AND —
HEY ! WE'RE GOING FAR FROM OUR PALACE.
BRING US BACK, GIRL !

SHINI DID NOT BRING THEM BACK. THEY SAILED AND SAILED TO A FARAWAY LAND, NEVER TO COME BACK. SHINI RULED THE KINGDOM WISELY AND WELL.

MAKING TREES BLOSSOM

Based on a story sent by:
Anil D'souza

Illustrations:
Goutam Sen

LO AND BEHOLD, IT WAS A POT FILLED WITH GOLD —
SHIRO! YOU CLEVER DOG! YOU'VE UNEARTHED A TREASURE.

THE OLD MAN TOOK THE TREASURE HOME, WITH SHIRO LEAPING AHEAD OF HIM. WATCHING THEM WAS THEIR NASTY NEIGHBOUR.
OH! THAT PESKY DOG HAS HIS USES, AFTER ALL! HE CAN SMELL GOLD.

NEXT DAY, THE NASTY NEIGHBOUR PUT ON AN ARTIFICIAL SMILE AND—
MAY I BORROW YOUR PET SHIRO FOR A DAY?
SURE, TAKE HIM BY ALL MEANS!

THE NASTY MAN RUSHED TO HIS FIELDS WITH SHIRO.
NOW FIND SOME GOLD FAST LIKE YOU DID YESTERDAY OR I'LL BEAT YOU BLACK AND BLUE.
SHIRO SNIFFED AROUND FOR A WHILE AND BEGAN DIGGING AT A SPOT —
AH! GOLD!! I CAN'T WAIT TO SEE IT.

BUT WHEN HE DUG FURTHER WITH HIS SPADE —

YECCH! THERE'S NOTHING HERE BUT SOME AWFUL, STINKING GARBAGE.

ENRAGED, HE TRIED TO ATTACK SHIRO WITH THE SPADE BUT IN VAIN.

SHIRO RAN HOME TO SAFETY. THANKS TO THE TREASURE THE OLD COUPLE AND SHIRO LIVED IN COMFORT FOR MANY YEARS...

...WHILE ENVY AND HATRED MADE THEIR NEIGHBOURS ILL AND THIN.

AS THE YEARS ROLLED BY, SHIRO BECAME QUITE OLD, AND ONE DAY —
HE DIED PEACEFULLY IN HIS SLEEP.
LET US BURY HIM IN OUR GARDEN.

LOVINGLY, THEY BURIED HIM IN THE GARDEN AND PLANTED A LITTLE APPLE TREE ON HIS GRAVE.

THE APPLE TREE GREW FAST AND SOON BECAME THE BEST TREE IN THEIR GARDEN.

ONE DAY, SEVERAL YEARS LATER—
DO YOU REMEMBER HOW MUCH SHIRO LOVED RICE CAKES?
LET US MAKE SOME RICE CAKES TODAY. I'LL CUT A FEW DRIED BRANCHES FROM HIS APPLE TREE.

THEY MADE A FIRE OUT OF THE DRIED APPLE BRANCHES AND COOKED SOME RICE CAKES ON IT.
AH! THE RICE CAKES HAVE TURNED OUT TO BE NICE AND FLUFFY!

BUT WHEN THEY BEGAN TO EAT THE RICE CAKES—
CRUNCH!
CLUNK!

THE RICE CAKES WERE FILLED WITH GOLD.
OH! OUR DEAR SHIRO HAS DONE IT AGAIN.
OUR POT OF TREASURE WAS GETTING OVER. NOW WE CAN LIVE WELL AGAIN.

THE JEALOUS NEIGHBOUR SOON HEARD ABOUT IT.AT NIGHT, HE STOLE INTO THE GARDEN AND BROKE OFF A FEW BRANCHES OF THE APPLE TREE.

GREEDY AS HE WAS, HE MADE SEVERAL DOZEN RICE CAKES ON THE APPLE WOOD FIRE—
COME, WIFE SEE THE MIRACLE YOURSELF! TAKE YOUR PICK OF GOLD-FILLED RICE CAKES.

BUT AS SOON AS HE SPLIT THE RICE CAKE—
UGH! YECH!! WHAT AN AWFUL SMELL!!
THE SAME GARBAGE THAT SHIRO LED ME TO, TWO YEARS AGO.

IN A RAGE, HE RAN OUT AND HACKED THE APPLE TREE TO PIECES AND SET IT ON FIRE—
SERVES YOU RIGHT, YOU WILY SHIRO! THERE'LL BE NO TRACE OF YOU NOW.

NEXT MORNING—
OH! MY BELOVED TREE HAS TURNED TO ASHES!
LET'S KEEP THE ASHES IN MEMORY OF SHIRO.

IT WAS WINTER, AND ALL THE CHERRY TREES IN THEIR ORCHARD WERE BARE—
NO, LET'S SCATTER THE ASHES IN THE CHERRY ORCHARD.
AH! YES. SHIRO LOVED TO PLAY AMONG THE CHERRY TREES.

AS SOON AS HE SCATTERED THE ASHES ONTO THE CHERRY TREES...

...THEY BURST INTO FULL BLOOM! EVERYONE CAME TO SEE THIS MIRACLE—
YOURS IS THE ONLY GARDEN IN BLOOM!

SOON THE PRINCE HEARD OF THIS MIRACLE. HE LOVED A PRINCESS BUT SHE HAD INSISTED THAT HE FETCH HER A BUNCH OF CHERRY BLOSSOMS FROM HIS GARDEN.
CAN YOU MAKE MY TREE BLOOM IN WINTER? I'LL GIVE YOU ANY-THING IN RETURN.
SURELY, I'LL COME RIGHT AWAY.

JUST A HANDFUL OF ASHES ON THE ROYAL GARDEN WAS ENOUGH—
AH! THE TREE IS FULL OF CHERRY BLOSSOMS. THANK YOU, KIND SIR.

THE PRINCE GAVE THE OLD MAN MANY RICH PRESENTS AND ALSO A TITLE.
HENCE FORTH YOU'LL BE KNOWN AS SIR-OLD-MAN WHO-MAKES-TREES-BLOSSOM.
ALL THANKS TO MY DEAR SHIRO.

THE ISLAND OF THE OGRES

Based on a Japanese Folktale sent by:

Ahmad Saad Akhtar

Illustrations:

Sanjiv Waeerkar

THE OLD WOMAN PUT THE PEACH IN HER WASHING BASKET AND HURRIED HOME TO HER HUSBAND.
LOOK, THE RIVER GOD HAS GIVEN US A GIANT PEACH.
I HAVE NEVER SEEN ANYTHING LIKE IT BEFORE.

SHOULD WE TAKE IT TO THE MARKET AND SEE IF WE CAN GET A GOOD PRICE FOR IT ?
WE SHOULD NOT SELL WHAT HAS BEEN GIFTED TO US. WE WILL EAT IT OURSELVES. BRING A KNIFE.

BUT JUST AS THE WOODCUTTER WAS ABOUT TO SLICE OPEN THE FRUIT, THE PEACH OPENED BY ITSELF.
OH!
AH!

BEFORE THEM LAY A VERY BEAUTIFUL LITTLE BABY BOY.
IT'S A BABY BOY. MY WISH HAS COME TRUE.

THEY NAMED THE BABY MOMOTARO OR LITTLE PEACH BOY. THE OLD COUPLE WERE THE HAPPIEST PEOPLE IN KURUSU AS THEY WATCHED THE CHILD GROW UP IN THEIR LOVING CARE.
STEADY, MY SON. ONE STEP AT A TIME.

THE YEARS PASSED AND MOMOTARO GREW TALL AND STRONG. ONE DAY WHEN HE WAS FIFTEEN YEARS OLD—
WHAT IS THAT NOISE MY SON?
IT IS FROM THE VILLAGE, FATHER. THE OGRES ARE ATTACKING THE PEOPLE ONCE MORE.

THOSE OGRES HAVE NOT LET THE VILLAGE PROSPER IN ALL THESE YEARS.
THEN WHY DON'T THE PEOPLE FIGHT THEM?

FIGHT AGAINST THE OGRES! THAT'S IMPOSSIBLE. THEY KNOW WICKED MAGIC.
LET ME GO AND FIGHT THEM, FATHER.

YOU CANNOT! YOU ARE ONLY A BOY.
IF THE OGRES HAVE MAGICAL POWERS, SO HAVE I.
THE WOODCUTTER KNEW THAT HIS SON SPOKE THE TRUTH. AFTER ALL HE WAS NOT AN ORDINARY BOY.

MOMOTARO CONVINCED HIS PARENTS THAT HE COULD FACE THE OGRES.
TAKE THESE THREE RICE BALLS WITH YOU, SON. YOU WILL NEED THEM.
THANK YOU, MOTHER. I'LL RETURN WITH SUCH WEALTH THAT YOU WILL NEVER HAVE TO WORRY ABOUT ANYTHING AGAIN.

MOMOTARO SET OFF ON HIS JOURNEY TO THE ISLAND OF THE OGRES. ON THE WAY —
HELLO, FRIENDS. WHY DO YOU LOOK SO WEAK AND SAD?
WE HAVE NOT EATEN FOR TWO DAYS AND ARE VERY HUNGRY.
THE YOUNG PEACH BOY HAD THE POWER TO UNDER-STAND THE LANGUAGE OF ANIMALS.

HERE ARE THREE RICE BALLS THAT MY MOTHER GAVE ME. EAT IT, YOU'LL BE STRONG AGAIN.
WHAT WILL YOU EAT?

DO NOT WORRY ABOUT THAT. COME, TAKE IT AND EAT.

AFTER THE THREE HAD EATEN THEIR FILL —
YOU ARE VERY KIND. WE KNOW THAT YOU ARE GOING TO DESTROY THE OGRES. TAKE US WITH YOU, WE MIGHT BE OF SOME HELP.
THAT WOULD BE WONDERFUL. DO COME ALONG!

AFTER WALKING FOR A DAY ALONG THE BANKS OF THE RIVER KISO —

THE SEA! THERE IS THE ISLAND OF THE OGRES. HOW CAN WE GET ACROSS?

ASK YOUR MOTHER, THE RIVER KISO. SHE WILL GIVE YOU THE ANSWER.

SOON THEY WERE INSIDE THE GATE.
HURRY, THE GUARDS HAVE GONE IN FOR THEIR MEAL.
LET ME LEAD THE WAY. I CAN SNIFF OUT THE OGRES.

THE RACCOON DOG LED THEM THROUGH DARK AND COLD PASSAGES TO A BIG HALL.
THEY SEEM TO BE BUSY WITH THEIR WINE AND FOOD.
HUSH! LISTEN TO WHAT THEIR CHIEF IS SAYING.

...AND WHILE WE HAVE THIS SECRET STRENGTH, NO ONE CAN HARM US.
SO LET US DRINK TO OUR HORNS!

CHEERS!
HORNS? SECRET OF THEIR STRENGTH? I THINK I CAN GUESS WHAT THEY ARE TALKING ABOUT. CAN YOU?

YES, THEIR STRENGTH LIES IN THEIR HORNS...
...AND THOSE MUST BE REMOVED. NOW LISTEN TO ME.

THE RACCOON DOG, THE MACAQUE MONKEY AND THE MAGPIE LISTENED ATTENTIVELY.
BUT DO BE CARE-FUL, LITTLE PEACH BOY.

WHEN THE OGRES HAD FINISHED THEIR MEAL —
I AM GOING TO MY ROOM TO SLEEP. LET NO OGRE DISTURB ME.

THAT IS THE CHIEF. NOW IS YOUR CHANCE.
STAND BY, FRIENDS, AND WISH ME LUCK.

AS THE OGRE CHIEF STEPPED INTO THE PASSAGE WAY —

HO, YOU BIG UGLY OGRE. YOUR END IS NEAR FOR I, MOMOTARO, HAVE COME TO DESTROY YOU.

WH-WHAT!

LOOK HERE, OGRE CHIEF! I AM BEHIND YOU.
AAARGH! WHICH HUMAN HAS DARED TO STEP ON OUR ISLAND.

I HAVE, AND NOW THIS ISLAND WILL BELONG TO ME.
I'LL CUT YOU INTO PIECES.

YOU'LL HAVE TO CATCH ME TO DO THAT.
I'LL SMASH YOU IN A JIFFY.

MOMOTARO RACED UP THE STONY PATH TO A CLIFF WHICH HAD A STEEP DROP.
COME HERE, YOU WRETCH. I'LL HAVE YOU SKINNED ALIVE.
COME AND GET ME, YOU FAT-FACED OGRE.

MEANWHILE THE CHIEF OGRE'S ROARS HAD WOKEN THE OTHER OGRES.
MOMOTARO, LOOK, THE OTHERS ARE COMING.
QUICK, RACCOON DOG, DO YOUR JOB.

SNARL
AAH! YOU WRETCHED CUR.
SNAP

THE MACAQUE MONKEY LEAPT ONTO THE OGRE'S BACK.
YAARGH! LEAVE ME, YOU MANGY MONKEY.

THE MAGPIE FLAPPED ITS WINGS IN FRONT OF THE OGRE'S EYES AND HE WAS BLINDED.

OH! I'M SLIPPING. HELP!

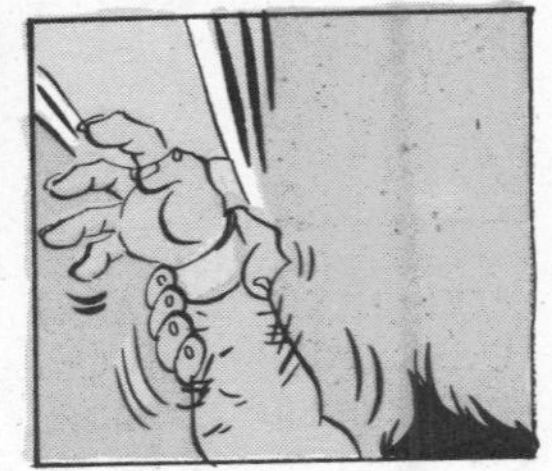

IF I LET GO OF YOUR HAND, YOU WILL MEET YOUR DEATH ON THOSE JAGGED ROCKS.
P-PLEASE DON'T LET ME FALL.

THEN, LISTEN. TELL YOUR OGRES TO STOP WHERE THEY ARE.
STOP! OGRES, STOP, OR YOUR CHIEF WILL DIE.

NOW TELL THEM TO PULL OFF THEIR HORNS AND THROW THEM INTO THE SEA.
B-BUT...

DO AS I TELL YOU OR YOUR END IS HERE.
ALL RIGHT! REMOVE YOUR HORNS AND THROW THEM INTO THE SEA.

WITH HIS FREE HAND MOMOTARO PULLED OFF THE CHIEF OGRE'S HORNS HIMSELF...

...AND FLUNG THEM INTO THE SEA EVEN AS THE OTHER OGRES DID THE SAME.
SPLASH
SPLASH
SPLASH

SUDDENLY, A REMARKABLE CHANGE CAME OVER THE OGRES.
WHY ARE YOU HOLDING A SWORD? IT CAN HURT YOU!
THROW AWAY THAT KNIFE, SON. IT IS DANGEROUS.

THE OGRE CHIEF, NOW A HANDSOME TALL MAN, REALISED WHAT HAD HAPPENED.
MOMOTARO, YOU HAVE RID US OF A TERRIBLE SPELL THAT WAS CAST OVER US TWO HUNDRED YEARS AGO.
YOU MUST THANK MY FRIENDS HERE TOO.

COME INTO THE CASTLE AND WE'LL CELEBRATE.
YES, LET US CELEBRATE OUR FREEDOM.

AFTER THREE DAYS OF FEASTING AND MERRYMAKING MOMOTARO AND HIS THREE FRIENDS RETURNED TO THE MAINLAND, LADEN WITH GIFTS.

THE OLD COUPLE WERE FULL OF JOY TO SEE THEIR SON SAFE AND SOUND.
WE THOUGHT WE'D NEVER SEE YOU AGAIN.
I'LL ALWAYS BE BY YOUR SIDE, FATHER. WE WILL NEVER BE POOR AGAIN.

THE RACCOON DOG, THE MACAQUE MONKEY AND THE AZURE-WINGED MAGPIE STAYED WITH MOMOTARO...
...AND THEY WERE GOOD FRIENDS TILL THE END OF THEIR LIVES.

THE PERFECT VISION

Based on a Japanese tale
sent by: Shivangi

Illustrations :
Archana
Amberkar

WE ARE NOT!
ALL RIGHT. LET US HAVE A BET TO FIND OUT WHO HAS THE SHARPEST VISION.
YURIKO ALWAYS PRIDED HIMSELF ON HAVING SUPERIOR INTELLIGENCE.

AGREED! WHAT WILL BE THE BET?
TOMORROW, AT DAWN, THE PRIEST WILL INSTALL A TABLET AT THE ENTRANCE TO THE TEMPLE.

... WHOEVER CAN READ THE INSCRIPTION WILL HOLD A SUPERIOR POSITION.

AT MIDNIGHT—
KNOCK KNOCK
WHO WOULD WANT THE TEMPLE PRIEST AT THIS HOUR?

IT WAS MIKO—
REVEREND FATHER, COULD YOU TELL ME WHAT IS WRITTEN ON THE TABLET YOU ARE GOING TO INSTALL AT DAWN?
IF YOU SO DESIRE...

... 'O EYES, SEE WHAT THOU OUGHT TO, O SIGHTLESS, DO NOT DESPAIR ....
THANK YOU, FATHER. GOODNIGHT.

FUNNY ! HE DID NOT LET ME COMPLETE IT.

JUST THEN—
MAY I COME IN, FATHER.
YES, KIKO. HOW CAN I HELP YOU?

KIKO MADE THE SAME REQUEST. SO—
'.... DO NOT DESPAIR. HEARKEN THE DOVES COO SWEETLY. LOOK WITHIN AND FIND ME THERE.' IT IS ENGRAVED WITH WHITE ON BLUE STONE.

THANKS AND GOOD NIGHT.
AT LEAST HE HEARD THE COMPLETE VERSE. MAYBE I CAN SLEEP NOW.

BUT—
OH NO... WHAT IS WRONG TONIGHT?
KNOCK KNOCK

IT WAS YURIKO, OF COURSE. AFTER HE HAD HEARD THE VERSE—
IS ANYTHING ELSE ENGRAVED ON THE STONE?
WELL... YES... THERE IS A WHITE DOVE ABOVE THE WORDS.

AT THE CRACK OF DAWN THE THREE FRIENDS ARRIVED AT THE TEMPLE—
LOOK, THE TABLET IS UP.
YES, DOESN'T THE BLUE STONE LOOK BEAUTIFUL!?

YOU CAN ONLY SEE THE COLOUR. WHAT ABOUT THAT LOVELY WHITE DOVE ABOVE THE POEM.
THE POEM ITSELF IS MORE BEAUTIFUL. DON'T TELL ME THAT YOU CAN'T READ IT.

AS THE THREE MEN QUARRELLED—
AHEM... EXCUSE ME.
... DO NOT DESPAIR.
ONLY THAT MUCH! I CAN READ THE REST.

WHAT IS THE MATTER, GENTLEMEN?
OH!
FATHER!

AFTER THE THREE MEN HAD EXPLAINED—
I AM SORRY BUT ALL OF YOU HAVE LOST.
WHAT!?

YOU'VE COME A BIT TOO EARLY. I HAVE NOT YET PUT UP THE TABLET.
OH!

THE THREE FRIENDS WALKED HOME SADDER BUT WISER. NOW, DURING THEIR TEA SESSIONS—
O EYES, SEE WHAT THOU OUGHT TO...
...O SIGHTLESS, DO NOT DESPAIR...
...HEARKEN THE DOVES COO SWEETLY. LOOK WITHIN AND FIND ME THERE.
THEY HAD LEARNT THEIR LESSON.

The Wisdom of the Choja

Script: Anomita Guha
Illustrator: Arijit Dutta Chowdhury
Colourist: Umesh Sarode

*TITLE GIVEN TO A WISE AND VIRTUOUS MAN

ONE DAY –
CHOJA, THE HARVEST HAS BEEN EXCEPTIONAL THIS YEAR !
WE'VE PLANNED A CELEBRATION TONIGHT, AND WE'VE COME TO INVITE YOU TO IT !

YOU MUST COME ! ALL THE VILLAGERS WILL BE THERE – YOUNG AND OLD !
AH, MY OLD BONES WILL CREAK IF I DANCE ! I WILL BE MORE COMFORTABLE RESTING AT HOME. ENJOY YOURSELVES !!

I'LL STAY WITH YOU, GRANDPA !
YOU SEE ? TADA WILL KEEP ME COMPANY, SO DON'T YOU WORRY ABOUT ME !

THEY DESERVE A CELEBRATION AFTER WORKING SO HARD THE WHOLE YEAR ROUND !

SUDDENLY –
WHAT'S HAPPENING, GRANDPA ?!
EARTHQUAKE.

DON'T BE SCARED, TADA. IT'S ONLY A MILD TREMOR. I HAVE SEEN EARTHQUAKES THAT WERE FAR WORSE !

YOU'RE RIGHT ! IT'S ALREADY STOPPED !

GRANDPA ?!

GRANDPA ! WHAT ARE YOU STARING AT ?!

LOOK AT THE SEA ! IT...IT SEEMS TO BE RUNNING AWAY FROM THE LAND !
!!!

THE VILLAGERS HAVE NOTICED IT TOO – THEY'RE ALL RUSHING TO THE BEACH !

WE SHOULD GO DOWN AND WATCH IT TOO !
NO ! MY FATHER'S FATHER TOLD ME OF A TIME WHEN THE SEA RAN AWAY... AND A TERRIBLE CALAMITY FOLLOWED !

I MUST ACT QUICKLY ! BRING ME A LIGHTED TORCH, TADA !

TADA WAS BEWILDERED BUT HE OBEYED HIS GRANDFATHER –
HERE, GRANDPA !

THE CHOJA TOOK THE TORCH AND HURRIED TO HIS FIELDS –
I PRAY THAT THIS WORKS !

USING THE TORCH, THE CHOJA SET ROW AFTER ROW OF HIS CROPS ABLAZE...

...UNTIL THE ENTIRE FIELD WAS A FIERY INFERNO !

GRANDPA ! WHAT HAVE YOU DONE ?! YOU'VE RUINED THE HARVEST !
SHHH, TADA.
THE FIRE BLAZED A FIERY RED AND SMOKE BILLOWED INTO THE SKY.
CHOJA'S FIELDS ARE ON FIRE !
LET'S GO TO HIS HELP !

THE CHOJA WATCHED ANXIOUSLY AS THE VILLAGERS RUSHED UP THE STEEP PATH TO HIS HOUSE.

HURRY ! HURRY !!!

SOON, ALL THE VILLAGERS HAD REACHED THE FIELDS –

CHOJA, WE MUST STOP THE FIRE !
HOW DID IT START ?!

(SOB !) GRANDPA DID IT ! HE STARTED THE FIRE WITH THIS TORCH !
WHAT ?! WHAT ARE YOU SAYING, CHILD !

OUR CHOJA WOULD NEVER DO SOMETHING LIKE THAT !
TADA IS RIGHT ! I STARTED THE FIRE ON PURPOSE !

LOOK YONDER AND YOU SHALL SEE WHY !

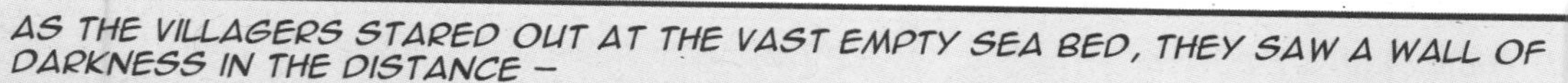

IT WAS THE RETURNING SEA, TOWERING LIKE A CLIFF AND MOVING FASTER THAN THE WIND !

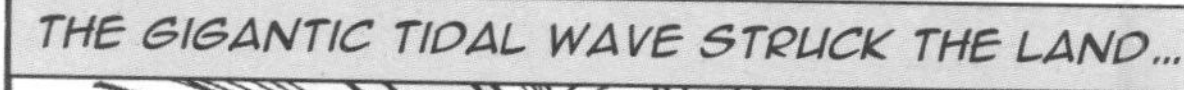

...AND THEN SLOWLY EBBED BACK...

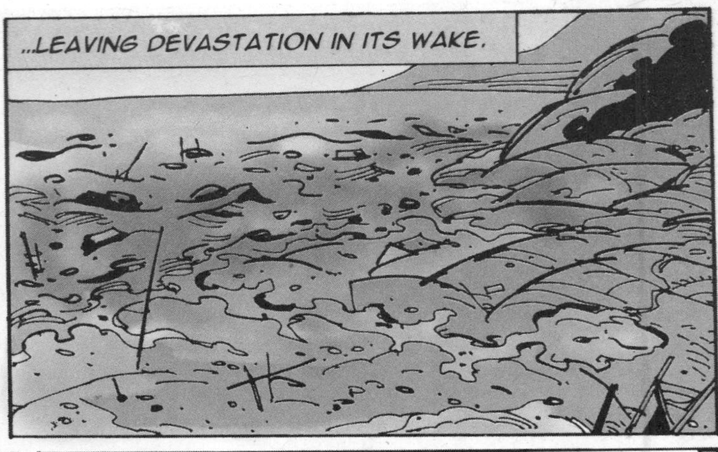
...LEAVING DEVASTATION IN ITS WAKE.

NOW YOU SEE WHY I HAD TO LIGHT THE FIRE ! I COULD THINK OF NO OTHER WAY TO DRAW YOU ALL FROM THE PATH OF THE TSUNAMI !
CHOJA ! YOU SACRIFICED YOUR CROPS, YOUR FIELDS TO WARN US !

WE WOULD ALL HAVE PERISHED IF IT WASN'T FOR YOU !
AND I WOULD DO SO AGAIN IF IT MEANT SAVING EVEN ONE LIFE !

THERE IS STILL GRAIN LEFT IN MY GRANARIES. WE'LL SHARE IT TILL THE NEXT CROP IS HARVESTED !

SLOWLY, THE VILLAGE LIMPED BACK TO NORMALCY, AND THE VILLAGERS WERE CHEERED BY A BUMPER HARVEST THE FOLLOWING YEAR. THIS TIME THEY REFUSED TO START THE PROCEEDINGS OF THE HARVEST FESTIVAL WITHOUT THE PRESENCE OF THEIR BELOVED CHOJA, AND FINALLY CARRIED HIM DOWN IN A TRIUMPHAL PROCESSION TO THE VILLAGE BELOW. THEY HONOURED HIM THUS EVERY YEAR TILL THE END OF HIS LIFE.